D1594925

The Chonky Alphabet by Victoria J Saunders

Published by Victoria J Saunders

@thechonkycollection

Copyright © Victoria J Saunders, 2022

All illustrations by Victoria J Saunders.

Formatted by Something Major Art

ISBN: 978-0-578-98696-8 (hardcover)

Printed in the United States of America

First Edition.

The CHONKY alphabet

by Victoria J Saunders

is for

ATTAC

is for

BLEP

is for

CHIMKINS

is for

DEMANDS

DEMANDS

- 🐾 scritches
- 🐾 pets
- 🐾 snamks
- 🐾 grooms
- 🐾 shrimpies
- 🐾 treats
- 🐾 chimkens
- 🐾 q-tips
- 🐾 tum tum rubs
- 🐾 attention

is for

ELEPHANT

is for

FLOOF

is for

GROMPY

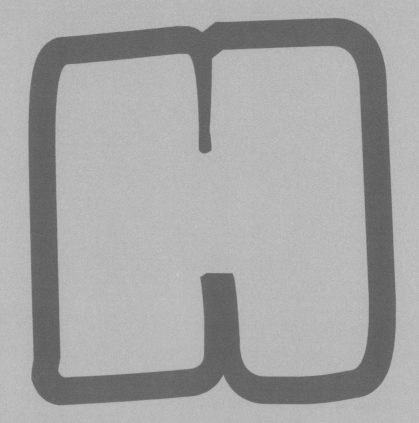

is for

HECKIN'
HOLLERZ

PLEASE REFILL

is for

IMMOBILE

is for
JONK

is for

KNEAD

is for

LOAF

is for
MEERKAT

is for

NIP NOPS

is for

OBSESSED

is for

PEETS

is for

QTIPS

is for

RELAGGS

is for

SHRIMPS

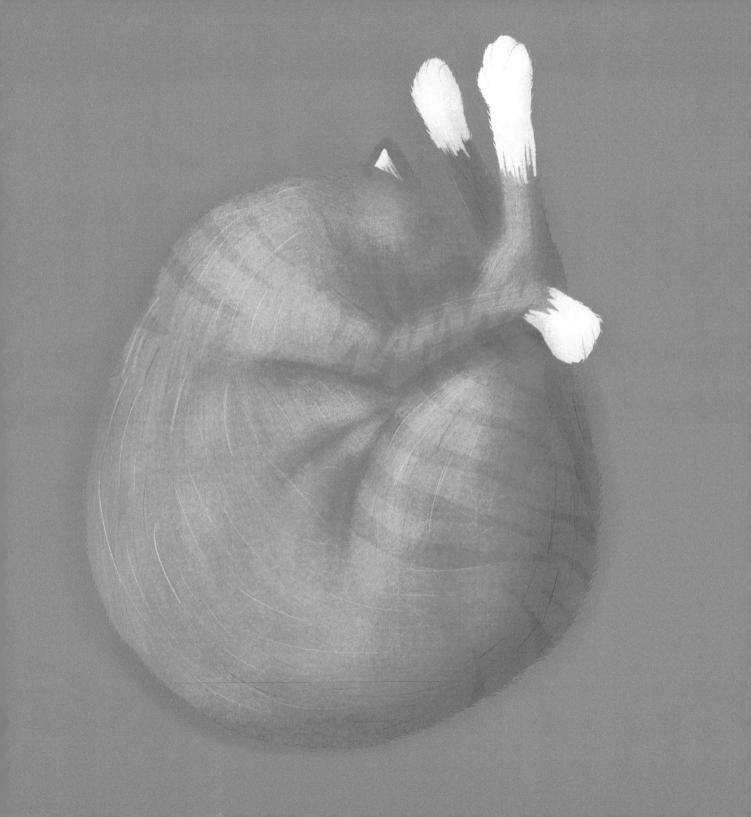

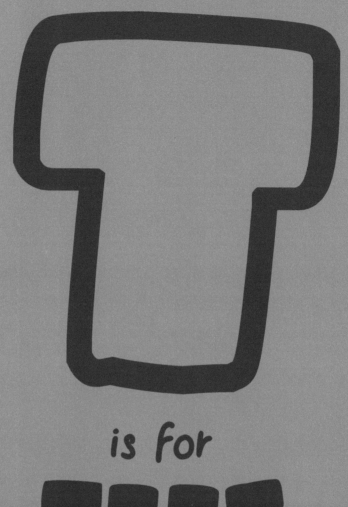

is for

TEEF

is for

UNIT

is for

VOID

is for

WRONG
ANSWERS
ONLY

is for

is for
YOGA

Z

is for
ZOOMIES

CPSIA information can be obtained
at www.ICGtesting.com
Printed in the USA
LVHW071643070722
722976LV00011B/344